CONTENTS

C000030673

A Warm-up

Write a word that rhymes with **day**.

1 _____

2 _____

3 _____

4 _____

5 Make the words into a sentence.

boy The went home.

_____

Add the missing letters.

6 b _____ of flowers

7 s t r _____ your legs

8 c a _____ the ball

9 Write a sentence using the word **frog**.

_____

10 Write a sentence using the word **pet**.

_____

B Word work

Add the missing letters.

ee ea

1 s p _____ k

2 d r _____ m

3 s t r _____ t

Use the words in these sentences.

4 This is the _____ where I live.

5 I can't hear you. _____ up.

6 Last night I had a _____ .

Underline the correct spelling.

7 luv   luve   love   lov

8 yur   your   yoor   yor

Write three words to describe

9 **a banana**

_____

10 **an apple**

_____

C Sentence work

Finish the sentence.

1 Nikki went to _____

2 The big dog _____

3 The ball _____

4 Denesh _____

Change one word so that the sentence makes sense. Write the new word. Cross out the old one.

5 Come back an help me. _____

6 Simon wet to see the old lady. _____

7 In the garden we was two magpies. _____

Write the sentence again but with capital letters in the correct places.

8 gemma and jack came to my party. _____

9 my teacher is called mr henderson. _____

10 today i am going to jordan's house. _____

X There is only one correct answer.   X There is more than one correct answer.

A Warm-up

The beginnings and endings of these sentences are mixed up.

The boy   opened.

The door   hissed.

The snake   grinned.

Write the sentences correctly.

1. _____

2. _____

3. _____

Write three words that rhyme with the word in **bold**.

4. **pick**   _____   _____   _____

5. **well**   _____   _____   _____

6. **ink**   _____   _____   _____

Add a letter to make a new word.

7. s e e __

8. t o o __

9. b e e __

10. t e a __

B Word work

Add the missing letters to make words that rhyme with **late**.

a i e

1. s k __ t __

3. w __ t

2. p l __ t

4. g r __ t

5. Add a letter to make three new words.

the __   the __   the __

Use the new words in these sentences.

6. Help _____ to carry it.

7. _____ are late.

8. Just _____ it stopped raining.

Write three things you might see at the seaside and three things you might do there.

9. Things I might **see**

_____

10. Things I might **do**

_____

C Sentence work

Complete the sentence.

1. _____ to play outside.

2. _____ made cakes.

3. _____ sat in the armchair.

4. _____ visited her friends.

5. What is wrong with this sentence? **There were three eggs. In the nest.**

_____

6. Write it correctly. _____

Write the sentence correctly.

7. The boy fell asleep. In the sun. _____

8. Ben shouted. From the window. _____

Add an adjective (describing word).

9. They set off into the _____ wood.

10. Suddenly, they saw a _____ bear.

X There is only one correct answer.   X There is more than one correct answer.   5

A Warm-up

Add the missing letters to make a new word.

1. t h e ___
2. t h e ___

3. Make the words into a sentence.

an A insect bee is

_____

4. Write four words that rhyme with **see**.

b ___   t r ___   g l ___   m ___

5. Which word is the odd one out and why?

_____

6. Underline the odd one out in these words.

cake   take   flake   break   lake

7. Why is it the odd one out?

_____

Complete the sentence.

8. _____ ate all the food.

9. _____ barked at the cat.

10. _____ found the gold.

B Word work

Add the letters to the correct word.

ow oa oe

1. b ___ l
2. g ___ s
3. g ___ l

Complete the missing word in the sentence.

4. Tom is my best fr _____ .

5. In winter it feels c _____ outside.

6. Come over h _____ .

These words are wrongly spelt.

pushin pullin jumpin

7. Why is the spelling wrong?

_____

8. Write the three words correctly.

_____

Add colour words.

9. Grapes can be _____ or _____ .

10. A zebra has _____ and _____ stripes.

C Sentence work

Add a word so that the sentence makes sense.

1. Omar _____ down the road.

2. The _____ sat on the wall.

3. He lived in a _____ house.

4. The _____ gave him a book.

Write a sentence using the two nouns (naming words) in **bold**.

5. **boy**   **gate**   _____

6. **girl**   **tree**   _____

7. **cat**   **playground**

Add full stops and capital letters.

8. we go swimming on monday

9. meet ellie at four o'clock

10. i am in the garden come and find me

X There is only one correct answer.   X There is more than one correct answer.

A Warm-up

1 Add the missing letter.

g i v __   l i v __   l o v __   h a v __

Use the three letters to make a word.

2 e o t   __ __ __

3 e i p   __ __ __

4 t o u   __ __ __

Finish the sentence.

5 This little duck _____

6 All ducks _____

7 One day the ducks _____

The same letter is missing from all these words. Write it in.

8 w __ s

9 h __ s

10 s __ i d

B Word work

Write the correct spelling.

1 nite _____

2 daytiem _____

3 flie _____

Add the second syllable.

4 sis __ __ __

5 chil __ __ __ __

6 num __ __ __

7 Write the words in alphabetical order.

_____

_____

_____

8 Add the **ing** ending.

float ___   splash ___   throw ___   catch ___

Use the words in these sentences.

9 I love _____ and _____ in water.

10 We were _____ and _____ the ball.

C Sentence work

1 Cross out the word **and** in this story.

the king lost his crown and he was very angry and everyone had to look for it

2 How many sentences are there now? _____

3 Write the story as separate sentences with full stops and capital letters.

_____

4 Write another sentence to go at the end of the story.

_____

Finish the sentence with an adjective.

5 The prince was very _____

6 The man was very _____

7 The bear cub was very _____

Cross out the word that is wrong. Write the correct word.

8 He fell of the swing. _____

9 He planted a row off sunflowers. _____

10 The lion is king off the animals. _____

X There is only one correct answer.   X There is more than one correct answer.

A Warm-up

Make three words using these letters only.

t a e

1 _ _ _ _

2 _ _ _ _

3 _ _ _

Add the missing letters.

4 g _ _ d   **Clue:** *not bad*

5 f _ s t   **Clue:** *not last*

6 l _ _ t   **Clue:** *not dark*

Write two sentences about dogs.

7 _____

8 _____

Write two sentences about bears.

9 _____

10 _____

B Word work

Add the missing letters to make words that rhyme with the word in **bold**.

o u e

1 **moon**   s _ _ n   J _ n _   s p _ _ n

2 **blue**   c l _ _   t r _ _   z _ _

3 **pool**   f _ l   s t _ _ l   _ l r _ l

Make these singular words into plurals.

4 frog _   5 spot _

Write the meaning of the word in **bold**.

6 The dog **hurried** into the forest.
'hurried' means _____

7 The girl saw something **gleaming** in the sunshine.
'gleaming' means _____

8 The boy **clung** to the rocks.
'clung' means _____

Cross out the word that is wrongly spelt. Write the correct spelling.

9 We had sum cake for tea.

10 I have won dog and a cat.

C Sentence work

There is a word missing from these sentences. Rewrite each sentence so that it makes sense.

1 Mum Dad read the newspaper. _____

2 It was dark cold in the woods. _____

3 I have a dog a cat. _____

4 Della could smell fish chips. _____

Add the full stops and capital letters.

5 finn and amy came to play we had a great time

6 it was late the sun had gone in

7 the ladybird was red it had black spots

Write a sentence using the verb (doing word) in **bold**.

8 **ran** _____

9 **jumped** _____

10 **swinging** _____

X There is only one correct answer.   X There is more than one correct answer.

A Warm-up

1 Write a sentence using the words **car** and **tree**.

_____

Change the vowel sound to make a new word.

2 l o a f → l ___ f **Clue:** *it grows on a tree*

3 b e a k → b ___ k **Clue:** *you read it*

4 m o a n → m ___ n **Clue:** *not kind*

5 Underline the odd one out.

hiss fuss yes pass

6 Why is it the odd one out?

_____

Complete the sentence.

7 _____ stood by the sea.

8 _____ lived in the cave.

9 _____ watching television.

10 _____ grows vegetables.

B Word work

The same vowel sound is missing from both the words below. Write it in.

1 jam j ___

2 shooting s t ___

Write the plural of the words above.

3 _____

4 _____

Look at these words.

calld pulld screamd

5 What is wrong with the spelling?

_____

Write the words correctly.

6 _____

7 _____

8 _____

Add the missing letters.

Clue: *they give us light*

9 c a n ___

10 s u n s h ___

C Sentence work

Make a question.

1 _____ is your name

2 _____ old are you

3 _____ do you live

4 _____ is your best friend

Change two words in the sentence. Write the new sentence.

5 Archie lived in a little house. _____

6 The little boy went into the street. _____

7 There was an old book on the shelf. _____

Underline the word that does **not** need a capital letter.

8 spain london town england

9 monday sunday friday today

10 luke i me danny

X There is only one correct answer.   X There is more than one correct answer.

A Warm-up

Make the words into a sentence.

1 **was the angry king**

_____

2 **sad little frog looked the**

_____

3 **had good man idea a the**

_____

Add the missing letters to make three words
that rhyme.

a o e

4 g ___ l

5 s t r ___ l l

6 h ___ l ___

Use the three letters to make two words.

o h w

7 ___ ___ ___

8 ___ ___ ___

The same letter is missing from these words.
Write it in.

9 w ___ e r e

10 w ___ i t e

B Word work

Make four new words by adding **er**.

jump buzz teach read

1 _____ 3 _____

2 _____ 4 _____

Write the missing word.

5 happily ever _____

6 _____ upon a time.

7 Underline the odd one out.

Far, far away …

A long, long time ago …

Today it is very …

There was once …

8 Why is it the odd one out?

_____

_____

Add the missing letters.

9 Sun _____ Mon _____ Tues _____

10 Wed _____ day Th _____ day F _____ day

C Sentence work

Write the next sentence.

1 First we had PE in the hall. Then _____

2 Yesterday it rained. Today _____

3 Last week the children planted sunflowers. Now _____

4 The children fed the chickens. After that _____

Put a full stop or question mark at the end of each sentence.

5 Where are we going _____

6 We are going to be late _____

7 It is nearly four o'clock _____

8 Will we get there on time _____

Cross out the word that is wrong. Write the correct word.

9 We are go to the zoo on Monday. _____

10 He is play outside. _____

Ⓧ There is only one correct answer.   Ⓧ There is more than one correct answer.

A Warm-up

Add the missing letters.

ou ow

1. b r _ _ n
2. s h _ _ t
3. t _ _ n
4. g r _ _ l
5. l _ _ d
6. f _ _ n d

7. Make the words into a question.

   the garden is that who in

   _____

Write three words that rhyme with the word in **bold**.

8. **catch** _____

9. **each** _____

10. Write four question words starting with **wh**.

    _____

    _____

    _____

B Word work

Which words have the same spelling pattern?

stood could good would

1. _____ and _____
2. _____ and _____

The same letter is missing from both words. Write it in.

3. _ i t t e n   4. _ e t t l e

Write the meaning of the words in **bold**.

5. The letter had been **scrunched up** and thrown away.

   'scrunched up' means _____

6. Suddenly the ground began to **quake**.

   'quake' means _____

7. The people were **alarmed**.

   'alarmed' means _____

Cross out the word that is wrongly spelt. Write the correct spelling.

8. We playd games. _____

9. I like singin. _____

10. Last night it snowd. _____

C Sentence work

Josh has been out. Write four questions to ask him.

1. _____
2. _____
3. _____
4. _____

Add a verb that fits the sentence.

5. The dog _____ in the pond and got wet.

6. Raindrops _____ on the windows all night.

7. The animals _____ in the woods for many years.

Cross out one **and**. Write two separate sentences.

8. the robot went crazy and it was rushing round the room and bleeping

9. Ben was lost in the wood and he was cold and hungry

10. She sat by the tree and something fell on her head and it was an acorn

X There is only one correct answer.   X There is more than one correct answer.

A Warm-up

Change the vowel sound to make a new word.

1 h o r s e → h _____ s e   *Clue: live in it*

2 b o o t → b _____ t   *Clue: sail it*

3 b i k e → b _____ k   *Clue: read it*

4 Write a question using these words.

   where bird

   _____

The same vowel sound is missing from both rhyming words. Write it in.

5 h _____ d   b r _____ d

6 t _____ m   s c r _____ m

Add different words to make four sentences.

7 The _____ stood by the _____ .

8 The _____ stood by the _____ .

9 The _____ stood by the _____ .

10 The _____ stood by the _____ .

B Word work

Add the missing letter.

1 h a p p _____

2 r e p l _____

3 v e r _____

Add the second syllable.

Clue: parts of a house

4 w i n _____ _____ _____

5 g u t _____ _____ _____

6 b a l _____ _____ _____ y

Add the words from questions 4 to 6 to the correct sentence.

7 Let's sit on the _____ .

8 A _____ is made of glass.

9 The rain runs into the _____ .

10 Write the sentence correctly.

   We saw six car and two bus.

   _____

C Sentence work

1 Why is an exclamation mark used at the end of these sentences?

   It's a goal!   Brilliant!   I've won!

   _____

Write each noun phrase as a complete sentence.

2 Our computer   _____

3 Class Three   _____

4 Mrs Shah   _____

Cross out the word that is wrong. Write the correct word.

5 Were are the cakes for tea?   _____

6 What are you wait for?   _____

7 Why saw the bus late?   _____

Put the capital letters into the sentence.

8 molly told polly and polly told me.

9 monday is mrs murphy's washing day.

10 david and daisy went to help mr jones.

X There is only one correct answer.   X There is more than one correct answer.

A Warm-up

Add the missing letters so that the words rhyme.

o e w

1 g r _____

2 t _____

3 s n _____

Add **er** to the verb. Write the new word.

4 paint _____

5 row _____

6 sing _____

Finish the sentence.

7 The bird flapped and _____

8 The girl looked and _____

9 It was dark and _____

10 Add the second syllable.

S a t _____ d a y

B Word work

Add the correct spelling of the vowel sound.

ore or

1 s c _____

2 s p _____ t

3 s h _____

4 s c _____ n

Write the meaning of the word in **bold**.

5 The fox had a **crafty** plan.

'crafty' means _____

6 He saw three **speckled** hens.

'speckled' means _____

7 The other foxes were **impressed** with his idea.

'impressed' means _____

Add an adjective and a plural noun to write phrases like this.

ten tired tigers

8 seven _____

9 five _____

10 two _____

C Sentence work

Write a question to go with the answer.

1 _____   Answer: It was sunny every day.

2 _____   Answer: It has four sides.

3 _____   Answer: We go back to school on Tuesday.

4 _____   Answer: Because I was cold.

The beginnings and endings of these sentences are mixed up.

The baby cried   **in the trees.**
Birds were singing   **under the water.**
The frog dived   **in his pushchair.**

Write the sentences correctly.

5 _____

6 _____

7 _____

Check and correct the sentence.

8 i saw a dragon. in the wood.

9 he ran has fast has he could.

10 the tide is go out

X There is only one correct answer.   X There is more than one correct answer.

A Warm-up

Add the missing vowel sound.

Clue: colours

1. b r _ _ n
2. b l _ _
3. p _ _ p l e
4. g r _ _ n

5. Write a question using these words.
present party

6. Underline the odd one out.

soon   fool   noon   good

7. Why is it the odd one out?

Add a letter to make a new word.

8. _ v e r y
9. _ a n y
10. _ o u r

B Word work

Add the missing vowels.

a e i u

1. s c r _ p
2. t _ b
3. s l _ m e

Use the words in these sentences.

4. _____ the mud off your boots.
5. The snail left a trail of _____ .
6. I need a _____ of toothpaste.

Cross out the word that is wrongly spelt.
Write the correct spelling.

7. She jumpt off the wall. _____
8. He pusht the door. _____
9. They helpt the man. _____

10. Underline the two phrases that sound like a story.

a great big enormous …

a bee is an insect …

all of a sudden …

C Sentence work

Complete the question.

1. _____ lives here
2. _____ did Nessie do
3. _____ do you do
4. _____ is the sky blue

Complete these sentences.

5. A dog jumped over the wall and _____
6. The owl hooted and _____
7. Mum gave me a broom and _____

There is a word missing from the sentence. Use ↓ to show where the missing word goes. Then write the word.

8. A baby lion called a cub.
9. A triangle is a shape three sides.
10. Some can drive over rough ground.

X There is only one correct answer.   X There is more than one correct answer.

A Warm-up

Add an adjective that starts with the same letter as the animal's name.

1 _____ caterpillars

2 _____ frogs

3 _____ hedgehogs

4 _____ butterflies

Add the missing vowel sound.

5 n ___ t h

6 s ___ t h

7 ___ s t

8 w ___ s t

9 Put a tick (✓) by the sentence that is complete.

a sunny day

Today it is rainy.

10 Add the missing letter.

sna _ ch sti _ ch fe _ ch no _ ch

B Word work

Finish the missing word.

1 The boat was s _ _ _ _ _ across the sea.

2 A bird came s w _ _ _ _ down.

3 A leaf was f l _ _ _ _ on the water.

4 The lamb made a b l _ _ _ _ sound.

Add the missing letters. Write the plural noun.

Clue: they all have wheels

5 t r a c _ _ _

6 c o a _ _ _

7 c a r a _ _ _

Write three words to describe the object.

8 **balloon** _____

9 **stone** _____

10 **sponge** _____

C Sentence work

Write the next sentence. It should say what happened next.

1 Harry waited at the bus stop. _____

2 We played party games. _____

3 First they went to the shoe shop. _____

Add the adjective to the correct sentence. **gleaming wicked brave murky**

4 The _____ mouse spoke to the lion.

5 The _____ wizard cast his spell.

6 The _____ star shone high in the sky.

7 Something moved in the _____ shadows.

Add capital letters, question marks and exclamation marks.

8 where are sunita and lucy going

9 when was queen victoria born

10 splash what was that

Now complete Section 1 of the Progress chart on page 46.

X There is only one correct answer.   X There is more than one correct answer.

15

My day out

Think of a day out that you really enjoyed.

Write about what happened on your great day out.

Hints

Think about:

- where you went
- when you went
- who you went with
- how you got there
- what you saw
- what you did.

Check

- When you have finished, check through your writing.
- Have you remembered to use full stops and capital letters?
- Have you checked your spelling?

Alfie meets an alien

Read through this story.

Change anything that does not look or sound correct.

Hints

Think about:

- Do the sentences sound right?
- Are the full stops and capital letters in the right places?
- Do all the spellings look right?

one day alfie went to fech the milk. then he came bak and the streat lookt very

different. There were alien in the gardins one funne alien wos jumpin up

and doun alfie sed hello. to the alien the alien beept at him

Extra

Now write an ending for the story.

Check

- When you have finished, check through your story.
- Have you remembered to use full stops and capital letters?
- Have you checked your spelling?

A Warm-up

Finish the sentence.

① The angry man _____

② The lonely boy _____

③ The hungry girl _____

Add the missing vowel sounds.

a e i

④ r _ d _

⑤ l _ _

⑥ t _ l

⑦ Write the words in alphabetical order.

_____

_____

_____

Add the missing letters.

Clue: family members

⑧ m _ t h _

⑨ f _ t h _

⑩ b r _ t h _

B Word work

Add the missing vowel sound.

or aw au

① p _ _ _   ③ t h _ _ n

② d i n o s _ _ r

Use the plural of the above words in these sentences.

④ _____ lived long ago.

⑤ A rose bush has _____ .

⑥ A mouse has tiny _____ .

Write the two smaller words that make the compound noun.

⑦ greenhouse _____

⑧ weekend _____

Write the meaning of the word.

⑨ a 'greenhouse' is _____

⑩ 'weekend' means _____

C Sentence work

Put a tick (✔) if the sentence is complete. Put a cross (✗) if it is not.

① Lots of flowers _____

② We had fun on the swings. _____

③ Playing ball games _____

Rewrite one of the above with a cross beside it as a complete sentence.

④ _____

A verb is missing. Give two ideas for what it might be.

⑤ The boat _____ _____ in the stormy sea.

⑥ The people _____ _____ to the king.

⑦ The lion _____ _____ at the other animals.

Add full stops, capital letters and question marks.

⑧ who is that at the door it must be jack.

⑨ what is emma doing out there she will get cold

⑩ there was something moving in the bushes what was it

✗ There is only one correct answer.   ✗ There is more than one correct answer.

A Warm-up

Finish the sentence.

1 Alex was feeling _____

2 Sophie wanted to _____

Add **s** or **es** to make the word a plural.

3 k i t e _____

4 k i s s _____

5 Change one letter to make a new word.

s t i l e → _ _ _ _ _   **Clue:** took

Add the missing vowel sound.

Clue: you wear them

6 s c _ f

8 j _ _ n s

7 b _ t s

9 c _ t

10 Write the words in alphabetical order.

_____

_____

_____

_____

B Word work

1 What do you notice about the letters **ear**?

clear pear swear dear

_____

2 Add the endings **s** and **er** to these verbs.

bake _____ _____

drive _____ _____

Write in the missing syllable.

3 c a r _____   **Clue:** on the floor

4 c o l _____   **Clue:** bring together

5 f o r _____   **Clue:** lots of money

6 v a _____   **Clue:** disappear

7 s t a r _____   **Clue:** very hungry

Underline the two adjectives.

8 There was once a naughty little goat.

9 Sita was lonely and afraid.

10 A huge rock fell into the icy water.

C Sentence work

Complete the sentence.

1 She saw the ghost and _____

2 He went into the garden and _____

3 A bird sat in the tree and _____

Sad Sid is a character in a story. Write three questions about him.

4 _____

5 _____

6 _____

Write the missing word.

was were is are

7 I _____ pleased with my work last term.

8 Today the flowers _____ starting to open.

9 Ali _____ outside at the moment.

10 My friends _____ going to visit me yesterday.

X There is only one correct answer.   X There is more than one correct answer.

A Warm-up

Add the same letter to every word in the list to make three new words.

1. _ h e e l   _ h a t   _ h e n
2. _ h e m   _ h e r e   _ h e n
3. _ i t   s _ i p   _ i l l

Write two sentences about lions.

4. _____

5. _____

Write two questions about lions.

6. _____

7. _____

Add the missing letters in the compound noun.

Clue: *places animals live*

8. w _ _ d l _ n d
9. r _ _ n f o r _ t
10. s _ _ s h _ _

B Word work

Add the missing letter.

1. _ n o c k
2. _ n i f e
3. _ n e e

Choose the right word to use in these sentences.

4. The sky is _____ .   (blew blue)

5. I can _____ you.   (hear here)

6. I _____ first prize.   (one won)

Use these words to make two compound nouns.

sun week end set

7. _____   8. _____

Write two verbs that you could use in this sentence.

The boy _____ across the playground.

9. _____   10. _____

C Sentence work

Write the verb needed to complete the sentence.

1. Dogs _____ often kept as pets.
2. A sunflower _____ yellow.
3. For many years the people _____ happy.
4. The next day the frog _____ still there.

Finish the sentence.

5. The clock struck twelve and _____
6. The clock struck twelve but _____
7. Dan woke up and _____
8. Dan woke up but _____

9. What is wrong with this writing? **The house was old. And creepy.**

_____

10. Write it correctly.

_____

X There is only one correct answer.   X There is more than one correct answer.

English Skills Introductory Book

A Warm-up

Add the missing letter.

c k

1 w h i s __

2 s __ e t c h

3 s __ a l e s

Complete the sentence.

4 _____ in the kitchen.

5 _____ in the garden.

Add the missing vowel sounds to these compound nouns.

6 b __ t h d __

7 f __ __ t b __ l l

Put the letters in order to make a word.

8 u r o _____

9 m e c o _____

10 e n e v _____

B Word work

1 What do you notice about these words?

pair	wear	care
square	bear	hair

_____

_____

Write a word from question 1 that sounds the same as the word in **bold**.

2 **pear** and _____

3 **bare** and _____

4 **where** and _____

Write correctly the word that is wrongly spelt.

5 They startid to scream. _____

6 He liftid up the frog. _____

Write four adjectives you might use to describe a dragon.

7 _____   9 _____

8 _____   10 _____

C Sentence work

The beginnings and endings of these sentences are mixed up.

Some bears	have fur.
A polar bear	are brown.
All bears	live in the Arctic.
Polar bears	is white.

Write the sentences correctly.

1 _____   3 _____

2 _____   4 _____

Matt fell off the wall. Write three questions to ask about this event.

5 _____

6 _____

7 _____

Write the missing word. **and but or**

8 They ran and ran _____ still the giant followed them.

9 The boy hid _____ waited to see what would happen.

10 We can wait here _____ go inside.

X There is only one correct answer.   X There is more than one correct answer.

21

A Warm-up

Underline the correct spelling.

1. kichen   kitchen

2. whisper   wisper

3. nowing   knowing

Add a rhyming word to make a question like this one.

Does a cow meow?

4. Does a snake _____

5. Does a bear _____

6. Does a sheep _____

7. Does a crow _____

Use these words to make three compound nouns.

bed door way motor room

8. _____

9. _____

10. _____

B Word work

Add the correct letters to these words.

1. e l e ___ a n t

2. a l ___ a b e t

3. d o l ___ i n

Write two words that begin with **wr**.

4. wr _____

5. wr _____

Add **ful** or **ly** to make a new word.

6. soft _____   7. pain _____

Use the new word in a sentence.

8. The rain fell _____ .

9. His leg was very _____ .

10. Write the pair of opposites.

old gloomy new dull

_____ and _____

C Sentence work

Write a sentence with the three words in it.

1. **clown and laugh** _____

2. **juice but cup** _____

3. **house but door** _____

4. **lion when people** _____

Put the capital letters into the sentence.

5. on friday miss muffet went to see humpty dumpty.

6. on saturday goldilocks went to see jack horner.

7. on sunday everyone was tired. they all stayed at home.

Write the correct word.

Finally First Next

8. _____ , pour some cornflakes into a bowl.

9. _____ , add some cold milk.

10. _____ , you can enjoy your breakfast.

X There is only one correct answer.   X There is more than one correct answer.

A Warm-up

1. Underline the odd one out.

   score   wore   floor   tore

2. Why is it the odd one out?

   _____

A verb is missing. Give two ideas for what it might be.

3. Ollie _____ the cakes.

4. The gorilla _____ in the tree.

5. The ghost _____ around us.

Write the correct spelling.

6. shoutid _____

7. jumpt _____

8. growlin _____

9. Write a sentence about popcorn.

   _____

10. Write a question about popcorn.

    _____

B Word work

Add the suffix to make a new word.

ful less ly

1. c h e e r _____

2. c l e a r _____

3. s p e e c h _____

Use the words in these sentences.

4. I saw it _____ .

5. Joe is always bright and _____ .

6. The shock left me _____ .

Underline the correct spelling of these compound nouns.

7. eyesite   Isight   eyesight

8. doorstep   dorstep   dorestep

Write the meaning of the word in **bold**.

9. A bus is **designed** to carry many people.

   'designed' means _____

10. The handle is **attached** to the door.

    'attached' means _____

C Sentence work

The child went to her granny's house and there was no-one there.

1. Write two sentences instead of using **and**. _____

   _____

2. Write the two sentences as one. Use the word **but**. _____

   _____

3. Write the next sentence in the story. Use the word **and** or **but**. _____

   _____

Write the missing verb.   **eat catches bakes throw**

4. She _____ cakes.

5. They _____ lots of cakes.

6. I _____ the ball.

7. He _____ the ball.

Add question marks, exclamation marks and capital letters to these jokes.

8. what do you call a tiny bee a babee

9. what game do cows play moosical chairs

10. how do you start an insect race one two flea go

X There is only one correct answer.   X There is more than one correct answer.

23

A Warm-up

Add the same letter to all these words to make new words.

1 _ n i g h t

2 _ n o w

3 _ n e w

Write three words that rhyme with the word in **bold** and have the same spelling pattern.

4 **my** _____ _____ _____

5 **old** _____ _____ _____

Finish the sentence.

6 The box was open but _____

7 He shouted but _____

8 Emily was scared but _____

Write in the missing syllable.

Clue: *found in a non-fiction book*

9 head _____ **Clue:** *at the top of a page*

10 cap _____ **Clue:** *goes with a picture*

B Word work

Write a word that rhymes with the word in **bold**.

1 **able** _____

2 **tickle** _____

3 **muddle** _____

Underline the correct spelling.

4 takeing takin taking takking

5 smiling smileing smilling smilin

6 comeing comming comig coming

Add **un** or **dis** to make the opposite.

7 lucky and _____

8 agree and _____

Add one of the words you have just made.

9 Tom and Megan sometimes _____ .

10 The team was _____ in the match.

C Sentence work

Make a question.

1 _____ the five senses

2 _____ Stoke on the map

3 _____ the captain of the football team

4 _____ you going on holiday

Make the sentence into two separate sentences.

5 He opened the door and went inside and it was dark.

6 He returned home and gave the gold to his wife and she was very happy.

7 It was late and starting to get dark and they were still far from home.

Finish the sentence.

8 It was very hot outside so _____

9 A tiger has escaped from the zoo so _____

10 It is nearly bedtime but _____

X There is only one correct answer.   X There is more than one correct answer.

A Warm-up

Add the same vowel sound to all these words.

1 m _ _ n i n g s t _ _ m f _ _ k

2 Write two other spellings of this sound.

_____ and _____

Write a sentence using these words.

3 **park but rain**

_____

4 **happy but sad**

_____

Add **un** or **dis** to make the opposite.

5 happy   _____

6 appear   _____

7 selfish   _____

8 loved   _____

9 honest   _____

10 Put the letters in order to make two words.

a e d r

_____ and _____

B Word work

Underline the odd one out.

1 jam   jog   gem   jug

2 It is the odd one out because

_____

3 city   sand   sums   soap

4 It is the odd one out because

_____

5 Write two words with the same ending as litt**le**.

_____ and _____

Add the vowel sounds to the compound nouns.

6 f _ _ r g r _ _ n d

7 p _ _ n t b r _ s h

8 _ r m c h _ _ r

Write an opposite for each of these words.

9 far   _____

10 empty   _____

C Sentence work

Write the next sentence.

1 A snail is a small creature. _____

2 Cows live on farms. _____

3 Tim the tiger looked around. _____

4 Sam and Anya were scared. _____

5 Which of the sentences are in the present tense? Tick (✓) the numbers.

1   2   3   4

Add adjectives to the sentence.

6 The _____ girl ate all the _____ cakes.

7 Zac was a _____ boy with a _____ face.

8 Tick the sentence that is an exclamation.

What an amazing animal   What sort of animal is it

Write both sentences using the correct punctuation.

9 _____

10 _____

X There is only one correct answer.   X There is more than one correct answer.

25

A Warm-up

Use these words to make three compound nouns.

pop flake snow corn

① _____

② _____

③ _____

The beginnings and endings of these sentences are mixed up.

An elephant	**are tiny.**
A mouse	**were huge.**
Ladybirds	**is big.**
Dinosaurs	**is small.**

Write the sentences correctly.

④ _____

⑤ _____

⑥ _____

⑦ _____

Add vowel sounds to make different words.

⑧ m _ n   m _ n   m _ n

⑨ f _ l   f _ l   f _ l

⑩ t _ n   t _ n   t _ n

B Word work

Add another word to make a compound noun.

① f a r m _____

② g o a l _____

Complete the word sum.

③ **hide + ing =** _____

④ **make + ing =** _____

Underline the adjective.

⑤ a ghastly monster

⑥ a wise man

⑦ a kind nurse

Write each adjective next to its opposite.

⑧ cruel → _____

⑨ foolish → _____

⑩ lovely → _____

C Sentence work

The magic rose is the title of a story.

Write five questions that the story might answer.

① _____

② _____

③ _____

④ _____

⑤ _____

Finish the sentence in three different ways.

⑥ The old man was tired so _____

⑦ The old man was tired but _____

⑧ The old man was tired and _____

Underline the word that is wrong. Write the correct word.

⑨ We went to the zoo and see lots of animals. _____

⑩ They raced across the sand and runs into the sea. _____

X There is only one correct answer.   X There is more than one correct answer.

A Warm-up

Use these words to make three compound nouns.

card code board post

1 _____

2 _____

3 _____

Add the missing letters.   *Clue: places*

4 s c _____ l

5 f _____ l d

6 s _____ s i d e

Complete the sentence.

7 _____ but I

could not reach it.

8 _____ but it

was too cold.

Write two adjectives to describe the sun.

9 _____   10 _____

B Word work

Write the correct spelling.

1 middel _____

2 jungul _____

Write in the missing syllable.

3 p o w _____ f u l

4 f o r _____ f u l

5 h a p p _____ l y

Use each word in one of these sentences.

6 They all lived _____ ever after.

7 The magic was very _____ .

8 Jack was very _____ .

Write the meaning of the word in **bold**.

9 Many houses were **destroyed** in the fire.

'destroyed' means _____

10 The castle is now a **ruin**.

a 'ruin' is _____

C Sentence work

Finish the sentences to continue the story.

1 They set off to find the palace. Before long _____

2 Then they had to go up a steep hill. After a long time, _____

3 At last they reached the palace gates. Suddenly, _____

Read the sentence. Write a word that is the opposite of the adjective in **bold**.

4 He lived in a **tiny** house.   _____

5 The children were **pleased**.   _____

6 It was a **sunny** day.   _____

7 The king was **kind**.   _____

Write the second sentence in the past tense as if the event has already happened.

8 They play in the garden. On Saturday _____

9 It is cold. Last night _____

10 Joe has three stickers. Last week Joe _____

X There is only one correct answer.   X There is more than one correct answer.   27

A Warm-up

Add the second syllable. **Clue:** *all pets*

1 h a m _ _ _

2 r a b _ _ _

3 g o l d _ _ _ _

4 Write the words in alphabetical order.

_____   _____   _____

Change two words. Write the new sentence.

5 The old man was clever.

_____

6 The path led to a little cottage.

_____

7 There was a tall tree by the fence.

_____

Add an ending to make three new words.

8 t i c k _____

9 n e e d _____

10 h a n d _____

B Word work

1 Add **ful** and **less** to the word **care**.

c a r e _____   c a r e _____

2 What do you notice about the words?

_____

Add **un** or **dis** to make the opposite.

3 _____ s a f e

4 _____ o b e y

5 _____ l o c k

Use the words in these sentences.

6 He could not _____ .

7 The teacher will _____ the room.

8 That wall is _____ .

Add the missing syllable.

9 l a w n _____ e r   **Clue:** *cuts grass*

10 h a i r _____ e r   **Clue:** *cuts hair*

C Sentence work

A verb is missing. Give two ideas for what it might be. Write the verbs in the past tense.

1 The children opened the door and _____ _____ into the street.

2 The man _____ _____ down the stairs.

3 The dog _____ _____ at the postman.

4 Snowflakes _____ _____ to the ground.

Complete the sentence.

5 _____ but it was getting late.

6 _____ or he would miss the bus.

7 _____ and jumped into the water.

Add punctuation and capital letters to these stories.

8 jack and jill were playing tennis tom wanted to join in

9 the bird saw the open window it flew into jessica's house

10 the fox jumped out the children screamed what a shock

28   X There is only one correct answer.   X There is more than one correct answer.

A Warm-up

Change the vowel sound to make a new word.

1 f e e l → f _ _ l **Clue:** *silver paper*

2 l e a d → l _ _ d **Clue:** *not quiet*

3 b o r n → b _ _ n **Clue:** *has hay in it*

4 s o i l → s _ _ l **Clue:** *found on a boat*

Write a sentence to say what happened next.

5 Harry hid behind the tree.

6 The rabbit hopped away.

7 It began to rain.

Write three words that rhyme
with the word in **bold**.

8 age

9 ice

10 race

B Word work

Add the suffix to make an adjective.

1 **peace + ful =** _____

2 **shine + y =** _____

3 **home + less =** _____

Cross out the word that is wrongly spelt.
Write the correct spelling.

4 He liveed here.

5 They danceed at the party.

6 They lineed up for lunch.

Write the meaning of the words in **bold**.

7 The giant **approached** the village.

'approached' means

8 His footsteps made the trees **tremble**.

'tremble' means

9 He **trampled on** Granddad's roses.

'trampled on' means

10 "I'm hungry," he **bellowed**.

'bellowed' means

C Sentence work

Continue these sentences in the past tense so that they sound like a story.

1 Long ago there

2 Far, far away

3 Suddenly, there

Cross out the adjectives that describe the character. Add words that mean the opposite.

4 Joe was a grumpy old man.

5 Ruby was a rich young lady.

6 Luca was a sad and quiet child.

7 The prince was poor but generous.

Write an exclamation to follow the sentence.

8 The giant jumped into the water.

9 The wizard gave him three wishes.

10 He bumped his knee.

Now complete Section 2 of the Progress chart on page 46.

X There is only one correct answer. X There is more than one correct answer.

Millie and the magic cooking pot

Write a story called **Millie and the magic cooking pot**.

Try to make it sound like a story you might read in a book.

Hints

Think about:

* How will your story start?
* What will happen in the middle?
* How will your story end?

Check

* When you have finished, check through your story.
* Have you remembered to use full stops, capital letters and other punctuation?
* Have you checked your spelling?

Letter to Jack

Read through this letter.

Change anything that does not look or sound correct.

Hints

- Do the sentences sound right?
- Are the full stops and capital letters in the right places?
- Do all the spellings look right?

Deer jack,

Thank you for comeing to see me on my burthday i hope you liket my jiant cake. And my jiant pizza. I now you like pizza.

i hope you find the gold coyn usefull we did haf sum gold egg. but the chiken keeps hideing them somewere.

it is mrs large's buthday in june we are going to haf a littul picnic. will you come and joyn us for that

With best wishis,

jim large

Extra

Now write an extra note from Jim, headed '**PS**'.

A Warm-up

Add the missing letters. **Clue: months**

1 M _ _ c h

2 J _ n _

3 D e _ _ b _ _

4 _ _ g _ s t

Josie screamed. Write three questions about this event.

5 _____

6 _____

7 _____

Change the vowel sound to make a new word.

8 t i m e → t _ m _
   Clue: not wild

9 w e e d → w _ _ d
   Clue: comes from trees

10 s e e n → s _ _ n
   Clue: in a short time

B Word work

1 Add the missing letters.

   Clue: parts of the body

   _ n e e c a p   _ r i s t
   a n _ l e   t h u m _

Add another word to make a compound noun.

2 _____ ground   3 _____ book

Write the meaning of the words in **bold**.

   The powerful rocket will go to a **distant** planet.

4 'distant' means _____

   Everyone hoped that the **fierce** animal would be **drowsy**.

5 'fierce' means _____

6 'drowsy' means _____

Add the correct suffix to make a new word.

ly less y ment

7 power _____

8 excite _____

9 fierce _____

10 speed _____

C Sentence work

Continue the sentence.

1 I stood on a chair so that _____

2 You will be hungry if _____

3 There is a zebra crossing so _____

4 A cup has a handle so _____

Cross out the adjectives. Write words that mean the opposite.

5 The room was bright and cheerful. _____ _____

6 The land was cold and damp. _____ _____

7 He lived in a tiny old house. _____ _____

Underline the word in the sentence that should have an apostrophe. Write it correctly.

8 Lucys birthday is in April and mine is in July. _____

9 I went to Lukes house on Saturday. _____

10 I was in Mr Neils class last year. _____

 X There is only one correct answer.   X There is more than one correct answer.

A Warm-up

Add the missing letter.

g j

1   m a _ i c

2   _ i a n t

3   e n _ o y

Add a word. It should rhyme with the word in **bold**.

4   This **goat** has a _____ .

5   This **whale** has a _____ .

Underline the correct spelling.

6   werk   work   wurk   wirk

7   theef   theaf   thief   thefe

Finish this sentence in different ways.

8   Now they were rich so _____

_____

9   Now they were rich but _____

_____

10   Now they were rich and _____

_____

B Word work

1   Make six words using these letters only.

w ar or d m th

_____ _____ _____

_____ _____ _____

Write these words correctly.

2   **Ive** _____

3   **dont** _____

Add the correct verb ending.

4   She went to the door and knock _ twice.

5   The room was empty so she walk _ in.

6   She saw the food and lick _ her lips.

7   He ran and dive _ into the pool.

Write the missing opposite.

8   People came from far and _____ .

9   The street was full of people, young and _____ .

10   Meena has an old car and a _____ one.

C Sentence work

Finish the second sentence.

1   The girl ran along the path. Meanwhile, _____

2   The old man went to bed. That night, _____

3   The lion lay down under the tree. Before long, _____

Add the correct verb form to complete the sentence.

ride stand switch lift

4   The man is _____ a bike.

5   Lots of people were _____ in the street.

6   They are _____ off the lights.

7   The wind was _____ the tent off the ground.

Add the full stops and capital letters.

8   We saw a snail it had a shell it moved very slowly.

9   Some old toys are clockwork you need a key to wind them up.

10   The castle is very old it was built on a hill so it was safe.

X There is only one correct answer.   X There is more than one correct answer.

A Warm-up

Change the vowel sound to make a new word.

1 s h o o k → s h ___ k
2 w a d e → w ___ d
3 s p e a k → s p ___ k

Add two adjectives to complete the sentence.

4 The _____ dog ran into the _____ cave.
5 The _____ lady drove a _____ car.
6 A football is _____ and _____ .

7 Underline the word that does **not** usually need a capital letter.

July   Snowy   Sunday   Amy

Add the missing letters.

Clue: parts of a plant

8 p e ___ l
9 l ___ f
10 f l ___ e r

B Word work

Write the ending needed to complete the words.

al el

1 c a m _____   m o d _____   t r a v _____
2 a n i m _____   m e t _____   p e d _____

Cross out the wrongly spelt words.
Write the correct spellings.

3 Eat harf a pear and a hole apple.

_____ _____

4 He waitid one our for the bus.

_____ _____

5 They plantid three pritty trees.

_____ _____

Draw a line to join the adjectives that have the same meaning.

6 smooth   huge
7 glad   happy
8 angry   surprising
9 big   furious
10 amazing   silky

C Sentence work

Finish the sentence.

1 A mango is sweet but lemons _____
2 Ants have six legs but a spider _____
3 Bicycles have two wheels but a tricycle _____
4 Some eggs are brown but _____

Use the sentence to write a **why** question.

5 Elena started to cry. _____
6 The ground began to shake. _____
7 Danny suddenly stopped talking. _____

Cross out the word that does not make sense. Write the correct word.

8 He was pick apples off the tree. _____
9 Mum was make a cake for tea. _____
10 I was go home in the dark. _____

X There is only one correct answer.   X There is more than one correct answer.

A Warm-up

Write three words that rhyme with the word in **bold**.

1 **who** _____ _____ _____

2 **high** _____ _____ _____

Write two sentences about clouds.

3 _____

4 _____

Write two questions about clouds.

5 _____

6 _____

Add **un** to write the opposite.

7 do _____

8 lock _____

9 tie _____

10 Make five words using these letters only.

m n r l ai

_____ _____ _____ _____

B Word work

Add **ful** or **ly** to make a new word.

1 c a r e _____   3 f r i e n d _____

2 l o n e _____   4 t e a r _____

Add one of these new words to the sentence.

5 Everyone was very _____

at the new school.

6 Be _____ not to break it.

7 The _____ little boy looked

sad and _____ .

Write two words with the same spelling pattern as the word in **bold**.

8 **fall** _____

9 **hedge** _____

Write one of these words instead of the words in **bold**. Check that it makes sense.

reach noticed return

10 He must **go back** home at once.

C Sentence work

Finish the sentence.

1 He would have to hurry or _____

2 She had to find somewhere to hide or _____

3 Always use suncream or _____

Add the commas.

4 At the farm we saw cows sheep ducks and chickens.

5 I like beans carrots peas and broccoli.

6 I had tuna cheese peppers and mushrooms on my pizza.

7 Why are the commas needed? _____

Add a word to complete the sentence.

8 I will climb to the top _____ it is safe.

9 I was happy _____ my team won.

10 He was cleaning the lamp _____ there was a flash of light.

X There is only one correct answer.   X There is more than one correct answer.

35

A Warm-up

1 Underline the odd one out.

moon   hoop   wood   food

2 Why is it the odd one out?

_____

_____

Write a word that rhymes with the word in **bold**.

3 **move** _____

4 **find** _____

Finish the sentence.

5 Today it is very hot but _____

_____

6 Today it is very hot and _____

_____

7 Today it is very hot so _____

_____

Add the missing letters.
Clue: places people live

8 v i l l _____

9 t ___ n ___

10 ___ i t

B Word work

1 Write the plural of these nouns.
   brick box toy teddy

_____   _____

_____   _____

Add **ly** to these words to make adverbs.

2 loud _____   3 brave _____

Write the word in **bold** correctly.

4 tidy and **intidy** _____

5 honest and **unhonest** _____

6 known and **disknown** _____

7 visible and **unvisible** _____

Write the meaning of the words in **bold**.

All the plants had **withered** and died, **except for** one. This plant is now tall and **sturdy**.

8 'withered' means _____

9 'except for' means _____

10 'sturdy' means _____

C Sentence work

Use these noun phrases to help you write three sentences for the start of a story.

a farmer   tiny cottage   lucky coin

1 _____

2 _____

3 _____

Use one of these adverbs to complete the sentence.

neatly slowly badly kindly

4 A snail moves _____ .

5 He hurt his knee _____ .

6 Josh spoke _____ to the little girl.

7 We wrote our names _____ .

Add capital letters and punctuation.

8 Write the address on the envelope stick a stamp on it put the letter in a postbox

9 Do you like chocolate lots of people do where does chocolate come from

10 There were once three rabbits called robbie bobby and ruby

X There is only one correct answer.   X There is more than one correct answer.

A Warm-up

1 Make six words using these letters only.

h n t ea ear

_____ _____ _____

_____ _____ _____

2 Write a sentence using these words.

play but ball

_____

These compound nouns have been mixed up.
Write them correctly.

crosscase   spacebrush   hairship   bookword

3 _____   5 _____

4 _____   6 _____

Write an adjective that describes the character.

7 There was once a _____ fisherman.

8 There was once a _____ king.

9 There was once a _____ farmer.

10 There was once a _____ lady.

B Word work

Add the missing vowel.

a i o

1 s l __ d e

2 h __ p e

3 a m __ z e

Add **ing** to the words you have made.

4 s l _____

5 h _____

6 a _____

Add the missing syllable.   *Clue: animals*

7 d o n _____

8 m o n _____

Write a word with the same meaning as the
word in **bold**.

9 The food has gone **bad**. _____

10 It was a **cold** day. _____

C Sentence work

1 Make the words into a statement.

play can football you

_____

2 Make the words into a question.

_____

3 Make the words into a statement.

found have answer you the

_____

4 Make the words into a question.

_____

Add an adverb ending with **ly** to complete the sentence.

5 We shared the sweets _____ .

6 The children lined up _____ .

7 The birds sang _____ .

8 The boy walked home _____ .

I saw a blackbird a crow a robin and a sparrow.

9 What is missing from the list of birds? _____

10 Write the sentence correctly. _____

X There is only one correct answer.   X There is more than one correct answer.

37

A Warm-up

1 Write two words with the same spelling pattern as the word in **bold**.

talk

_____   _____

Complete the sentence.

2 The dog growled and _____

3 The wise owl looked _____

4 _____

or in the garden.

Add the missing letter.

a o u

5 p r _ v e   w _ n t   b _ s y

6 m _ n e y   w _ s h   s h o _ l d

Add the missing syllable.

7 b e _____   *Clue: not in front*

8 f i n _____   *Clue: end*

9 s u b _____   *Clue: take away*

10 s e c _____   *Clue: not first*

B Word work

1 Underline the correct spelling.

flys   flis   flies   flyes

Make the words in **bold** into plurals. Some letters may need to be crossed out.

2 We sell **clock** _____ and **watch** _____ .

3 Wash all the **plate** _____ and **dish** _____ .

4 Meet the **mother** _____ and **baby** _____ .

Add the endings to the verbs.

add **ed**   add **es**

5 cry _____ _____

6 fry _____ _____

7 try _____ _____

Replace the crossed-out words with these.

recognised seized offered

8 They ~~knew~~ _____ him at once.

9 They ~~gave~~ _____ him a drink.

10 He ~~got~~ _____ the rope.

C Sentence work

Finish the sentence.

1 The boy asked for more bread because _____

2 Jade trusted the old lady because _____

3 The sun looks small because _____

4 Some people go jogging because _____

Write the adjectives to complete the noun phrases.

5 A _____ man waited by the _____ door.

6 She was wearing a _____ hat with _____ flowers.

7 The _____ puppy lay by the _____ fire.

Add the full stops and capital letters.

8 he ran and ran and ran finally he stopped he could run no more

9 lucy saw a lion the lion saw lucy the lion roared and lucy ran away

10 in december it is cold in august it is often hot

X There is only one correct answer.   X There is more than one correct answer.

A Warm-up

Change the vowel sound to make a new word.

1. g l o o m → g l ___ m   *Clue: shine*
2. b u r s t → b ___ s t   *Clue: show off*
3. s p o o k → s p ___ k   *Clue: tiny light*
4. f i r s t → f ___ s t   *Clue: big meal*
5. t u r n → t ___ n   *Clue: ripped*

Both words have the same ending missing.
Write it in.

6. s i m p ___   g r u m b ___
7. t u n n ___   l a b ___

Complete the sentence.

8. _____ but it

   was too hot.

9. _____

   so it was too hot.

10. _____ because it

    was too hot.

B Word work

Add the missing vowel sound.

1. s m ___ t h l y
2. c h ___ r f u l
3. p ___ c e f u l

4. Which word means **happy**? _____
5. Which word means **quiet**? _____

Underline the word that is wrongly spelt.
Write the correct spelling.

6. They went shoping. _____
7. Let's go swiming. _____
8. Everyone claped. _____

Write the meaning of the words in **bold**.

9. Sitting in the hot sun, the man **dozed off**.

   'dozed off' means _____

10. The jailer had a **grisly** laugh.

    'grisly' means _____

C Sentence work

Read this sentence. **Birds build nests.**

1. Is it a statement, a question or a command? _____
2. Give a reason for your answer. _____

Use these nouns and noun phrases to write statements.

3. ants – underground nests _____
4. hedgehog – spines, strong claws _____
5. baby goat – kid _____
6. wool – sheep – farms _____
7. lizard – short legs, tail _____

Cross out the word that sounds wrong. Write it correctly.

8. It was Bella birthday. _____
9. They went to the old man house. _____
10. They dug for gold in the farmer field. _____

X There is only one correct answer.   X There is more than one correct answer.

A   Warm-up

Write three words that rhyme with the word in **bold**.

1   **here**   _____   _____   _____

2   **war**   _____   _____   _____

3   **bird**   _____   _____   _____

Amina was going to the shop. What happened?

4   On the way _____

5   Suddenly, _____

6   When she got to the shop, _____

_____

Put these words together to make four compound nouns.

teller   book   story   case   shelf

7   _____

8   _____

9   _____

10   _____

B   Word work

Complete the word sum.

1   **pop + ed** =   _____

2   **sit + ing** =   _____

3   **like + ing** =   _____

4   **spy + ed** =   _____

Write the words as one word using an apostrophe.

5   it is   _____

6   I am   _____

7   do not   _____

8   did not   _____

9   Underline the word that means the smallest size.

    small   little   minute   tiny

10   Underline the word that means the biggest size.

    large   big   enormous   great

C   Sentence work

Finish the sentence.

1   Take a rest when _____

2   There was no-one there when _____

3   You can only build a snowman when _____

4   He was scared when _____

Write the sentence as a question.

5   We can go swimming.   _____

6   I can help clean the car.   _____

7   You do know Alia.   _____

Add three more items to the sentence. Add commas.

8   In my pocket I have a bus ticket, _____

9   In the winter I wear my coat, _____

10   You need a pencil, _____

X There is only one correct answer.   X There is more than one correct answer.

A Warm-up

Write the start of each sentence.

1. _____ when I am sleepy.
2. _____ when Sam woke up.
3. _____ when it rains.
4. _____ when we got to the top.

5. Make six words using these letters only.

   b c h l n ow

   _____ _____ _____

   _____ _____ _____

Add the missing vowel sound.

Clue: five senses

6. s _ _
7. h _ r
8. t _ te
9. s m _ l l
10. t _ c h

B Word work

Add **er** and **est** to these adjectives.

1. quick   _____ _____
2. sad   _____ _____
3. nice   _____ _____

Add the missing suffix.

ly ful

4. He said he would glad ____ help.
5. The hairbrush was use ____ .
6. They had a love ____ time.
7. The old man was forget ____ .

Write the pairs of words that have the same meaning.

leap   throw   jump

shiver   hurl   shake

8. _____ and _____
9. _____ and _____
10. _____ and _____

C Sentence work

Write the next sentence. It must follow on from the first.

1. Add the sugar to the flour. Next, _____
2. Jack slowly climbed the beanstalk. Eventually, _____
3. We stopped for an ice cream. After that, _____
4. Aziz sat in his armchair. Suddenly, _____

Complete the command.

5. Put _____
6. Hold _____
7. Wait _____
8. Don't _____

9. Add the apostrophes to the rhyme.

   Amys bike is new,

   Joes bike is blue,

   Katies bike is old,

   Bens bike is gold.

10. Add the capital letters to this address.

    mr james doyle

    51 hill street

    fordham fh5 3jk

X There is only one correct answer.   X There is more than one correct answer.

A Warm-up

Write the correct verb.

play loves washes clean

1 They _____ the windows.

2 She _____ football.

3 We _____ games.

4 He _____ the car.

5 Write three adjectives you might use to describe a wizard.

_____ _____ _____

Add the missing letter.

k g w b

6 ___ r o n g

7 ___ n o c k

8 c l i m ___

9 ___ n a w

10 Tick the vowel sounds that could go in this word.

b ___ ___ s t

u r   e a   a i   o a   o r

B Word work

Add the missing vowel sound.

ear air

1 a p p ___ ___ ___

2 c l ___ ___ ___

3 f ___ ___ ___

4 f ___ ___ ___

5 Which of the words above go with the suffix **ness**?

_____ ness   _____ ness

6 Which of the words above go with these suffixes?

ful ly

_____ ful   _____ ly

7 Cross out the words that are wrongly spelt.

The bizy bee flys rownd the garden agen.

Write the correct spellings.

_____ _____ _____

_____ _____

Add the missing ending.

8 fic ___   *Clue: made up*

9 sta ___   *Clue: where trains stop*

10 frac ___   *Clue: a half*

C Sentence work

Complete the sentence.

1 If you heat water in a kettle, _____

2 Owls are birds that _____

3 Most plants cannot grow in a desert because _____

4 Use water to wash your clothes when _____

Cross out the verb in the sentence. Use one of these verbs instead.

leap rush prowl soar flutter

5 A man jumps over the wall. _____

6 A bird is flying high above. _____

7 A tiger is walking in the grass. _____

8 A butterfly flaps its wings. _____

9 A river runs down the hill. _____

10 This is the beginning of a report. Check it for capital letters, full stops and question marks.

in july it is often hot and sunny in january it is cold why is this

X There is only one correct answer.   X There is more than one correct answer.

A Warm-up

Complete the sentence.

1. It was dark so
2. I was tired when

Add the missing letters in these compound nouns.

e a

3. n _ t b _ l l
4. b _ n s t _ l k
5. h _ d s t _ n d
6. s _ s h _ l l

Write in the missing endings.

7. t u r k _____   c h i m n _____   t r o l l _____
8. e m p t _____   f a m i l _____   l o l l _____

Rewrite the sentence using apostrophes in the correct places.

9. Im going to sleep at Emmas house.

10. I cant wait to see Joes new dog.

B Word work

Add the correct suffix.

ment ness

1. d a r k _____
2. e x c i t e _____
3. e n j o y _____
4. k i n d _____

Underline the correct spelling.

5. warter   worter   water   worta
6. wotch   watch   whatch   wach
7. wurld   werld   wirld   world

Write the meaning of the word in **bold**.

8. They were **astonished** by his idea.

   'astonished' means

9. "Stop!" **pleaded** the captain.

   'pleaded' means

10. The ship had been **wrecked**.

    'wrecked' means

C Sentence work

Finish the command.

1. Throw the dice. Then
2. Open your book. Now
3. Leave the cake to cool. Finally,

Add adjectives to describe the nouns.

4. The _____ girl crept into the _____ wood.
5. The _____ _____ man fell down the steps.
6. One _____ night, the _____ man ran away.

Underline what the character says.

7. "Are you telling the truth?" asked Salma.
8. "I don't like cabbage," moaned Sophie.
9. "You must keep your promise," said the queen.
10. "What is your name?" asked the teacher.

Now complete Section 3 of the Progress chart on page 46.

X There is only one correct answer.   X There is more than one correct answer.

43

How to keep healthy

Your task is to tell people what they can do to keep healthy.

Hints

Think about the information you need to tell your reader. For example, you might include:

- things to eat
- things to do
- what not to do.

Check

- When you have finished, check through your writing.
- Have you remembered to use full stops, capital letters and other punctuation?
- Have you checked your spelling?

Wendy the witch

Read through this story.

Change anything that does not look or sound correct.

Hints

- Do the sentences sound right?
- Are the full stops and capital letters in the right places?
- Do all the spellings look right?

There was wonce a little witch calld wendy and she livd in a tiny cottige. on the ege of the woods. She had green hair. And a green fase. She new lots of spells. But they was all good spells. She didnt make bad spells or poshuns.

Evry day she put on her hat cloke and pointid shoos and hurrid of into the woods wendy is happy and chearfull so the animuls was not scard off her she ulways stoped to talk when she sore them.

Extra

Describe the creatures that Wendy saw as she walked.

Name: _____   Class/Set: _____

Teacher's name: _____   Date: _____

Instructions

Read the **'I can' targets** for the section you have just finished.
- Colour the circle **green** if you find it **easy** to do what is described.
- Colour the circle **orange** if you are **getting there**, but still need to work on it.
- Colour the circle **red** if you still find this a **difficult** thing to do.

If there are things that you still find difficult, you can work on them in the next section or in the next book.

Writing sentences

'I can' targets	Section 1	Section 2	Section 3
I can write in clear separate sentences.	○	○	○
I can write questions, statements, exclamations and commands.	○	○	○
I can use words such as **and**, **but**, **so** and **or** to link ideas in a sentence.	○	○	○
I can use adjectives to add detail.	○	○	○
I can read through my writing and say where sentences start and end.		○	○
I can write longer sentences using **because**, **when**, **that** and **if**.			○
I can use adverbs to add detail.			○

Using punctuation

	Section 1	Section 2	Section 3
I can use capital letters to show where sentences start.	○	○	○
I can use full stops to show where sentences end.	○	○	○
I can use a question mark or exclamation mark when needed.	○	○	○
I can use capital letters for names, titles, **I**, days of week and months.	○	○	○
I can use commas in lists.			○
I can use apostrophes in words (e.g. **didn't**, **Jake's bike**).			○

Checking grammar

	Section 1	Section 2	Section 3
I can check that my writing makes sense.	○	○	○
I can use the right tense and keep to it.		○	○
I can use past/present verb forms correctly (e.g. **jump/ed**, **is/was**, **has/had**).		○	○

Understanding and choosing words

	Section 1	Section 2	Section 3
I can choose some interesting words for descriptions.	○	○	○
I can work out the meaning of a word from how it is used.	○	○	○
I can use some story language.	○	○	○
I can think of lots of different words to use in place of a given word.		○	○
I can use words to link events (e.g. **after**, **next**).		○	○
I can choose words to fit different types of text.			○

Spelling

	Section 1	Section 2	Section 3
I can segment words to help me spell them.	○	○	○
I can choose the right way of spelling a sound.	○	○	○
I can spell two-syllable words and compound words.	○	○	○
I can spell tricky words like **said**, **once**, **great** and **busy**.	○	○	○
I can use spelling patterns to help me spell words (e.g. **tch**, **all**, **dge**).	○	○	○
I can add **ing**, **ed**, **er** to the end of words such as **smiling**, **stopped**, **jumper**.	○	○	○
I can spell plurals by adding **s** or **es** (e.g. **pens**, **boxes**, **cries**).	○	○	○
I can choose the correct spelling of words that sound the same (e.g. **see/sea**).		○	○
I can add **un** and **dis** to words.		○	○
I can spell longer words with the suffixes **ful**, **ly**, **less**, **ness** and **ment**.		○	○